Beyond Words

Becky and Steve Schenck's Inspiring Story
of Faith, Hope, and Love in the Face of Terminal Brain Cancer

Written by
Lisa Abbott and Erin Sheets

Kristin —
You are such a gem ~
so glad that I've gotten
to know you.
All my best,
Lisa

Published & distributed by:
Steve Schenck

in association with:
IBJ Book Publishing, LLC.
41 E. Washington St., Suite 200
Indianapolis, IN 46204
www.ibjbp.com

Cover photo courtesy of *Indianapolis Woman* and PULSPhotography

ISBN 978-1-939550-42-2
Library of Congress Control Number: 2016942412
First Edition
Printed in the United States of America

DEDICATION

Beyond Words is dedicated, with gratitude, to:

God, who gifted Becky and Steve with a life full of love and laughter; and who, in His grace, exceeded their wildest dreams by granting them ten additional years of life together after Becky's diagnosis.

Becky, whose courage, indelible spirit, and positive attitude inspired the many, many lives she has touched.

The Schenck children, grandchildren, and the family's dear friends, who accompanied Becky and Steve on their journey with glioblastoma multiforme, and who make every day worth living.

Becky's medical "Dream Team," including Dr. Mitch Berger, Dr. Nicholas Butowski, Dr. Jennifer Morgan, Dr. Tim Kelly, and Margaretta Page, R.N. Each of these gifted individuals contributed their exceptional medical expertise to Becky's treatment with genuine concern and compassion.

The many other health care providers at University of California San Francisco (UCSF), Community Health Network, IU Health, and St. Vincent Hospice, who each played a role in Becky's treatment. They consistently delivered excellent, compassionate care for Becky throughout the course of her treatment.

Eli Lilly and Company and its global research team, for the incredible privilege of Becky's participation in a phase 1 clinical trial; and for the company's commitment to funding research and development of a drug to treat brain cancer. Lilly's experimental drug and the clinical trial gave the Schenck family hope in the face of a dire outlook.

Lisa Abbott and Erin Sheets, for their passion to share Becky and Steve's remarkable story.

INTRODUCTION

Absolutely nothing can prepare you to hear a doctor utter the unthinkable words, "You have brain cancer." Becky and Steve Schenck know this all too well. They will never forget the summer day in 2006 that abruptly changed the course of their lives. Becky, a healthy, active, vibrant woman in her fifties, was living life to the fullest. Her illness struck without warning. Her diagnosis of stage four glioblastoma multiforme–terminal brain cancer–left her and husband, Steve, in a state of shock and disbelief. Doctors gave Becky an initial prognosis of twelve to fifteen months to live. Suddenly, she and Steve entered a world in which they felt like foreigners.

The story that unfolded for the Schencks following Becky's diagnosis is nothing short of remarkable. The God in whom they believed and trusted aligned their circumstances and provided them with the people and resources that Becky needed to defy all odds. She was blessed with a decade of life beyond her prognosis.

Becky became a source of strength and inspiration to everyone whose life she touched, as she courageously fought back at the disease that had altered her daily existence. Her indelible spirit and unquenchable positive attitude moved everyone – from her friends, to her doctors and medical staff, to those who read or saw her story in the media, to those who heard her share her story firsthand.

No one was perhaps more inspired by Becky's faith and determination than her husband, Steve, who in time became her full-time caregiver. A new, urgent awareness of life's preciousness and their limited time left together brought unprecedented depth and intimacy to the love they had shared for nearly fifty years.

The difficult experiences deepened their faith in each other and in the God whom they loved and served. They learned to live each day from a place of hope, amidst the realities that accompany a terminal illness. Together, they lived out the truth they believed, that "Love bears all things, believes all things, hopes all things, endures all things" (I Corinthians 13:7 ESV). Given the option, they say, they wouldn't trade all they have learned together over the past decade for anything.

Becky and Steve's story inspired many people, even as it was unfolding. The narrative that follows shares the details of the Schencks' journey, told with the express purpose of encouraging and inspiring others who also find themselves in the unexpected place of facing a terminal illness. The Schencks offer helpful resources and insights from their own experience, for those who are living in the sometimes lonely, scary, confusing days that follow a brain cancer diagnosis. May this account become a source of hope and help to the community of patients, families, and caregivers who alone understand both the challenges and suffering, and also the unexpected moments of joy that are part of living with a terminal illness.

There is, the Schencks discovered, an inaudible language that emerges when verbal expression is limited or impossible. It is a sacred dialect of unconditional love that, in its expression, goes far beyond words.

TABLE OF CONTENTS

Chapter 1: Dinner at Table 514   1

Chapter 2: Something is Very Wrong   3

Chapter 3: Young Love   6

Chapter 4: We are Family   9

Chapter 5: Building a Legacy with Love for the Community   11

Chapter 6: A Grim Diagnosis   16

Chapter 7: Exploring Options and Fighting Back   19

Chapter 8: Assembling a Medical "Dream Team"   25

Chapter 9: Surgery in San Francisco   29

Chapter 10: Friends Express Their Love   32

Chapter 11: Hugs, Radiation, and Chemotherapy   34

Chapter 12: Life on Life's Terms   37

Chapter 13: A New Season of Caregiving   42

Chapter 14: Home, Where the Heart is   46

Chapter 15: Sharing the Journey   48

Chapter 16: Family and Faith   50

Chapter 17: Inspiring Others   53

Chapter 18: Defying the Odds   56

Chapter 19: Continuing the Fight   59

Chapter 20: Preparing for the End   63

Chapter 21: Beyond Words   67

Notes   70

Resources   72

CHAPTER 1

Dinner at Table 514

At a glance, table 514 resembles any other at the Ruth's Chris Steakhouse on Indianapolis' north side. On this February evening in 2016, it's draped in a crisp, white table linen. Its candles are lit and its places are elegantly set with flatware and water goblets for dinner guests. For the couple who has reserved this same booth many times over the past several years, it has become much more than a cozy spot to enjoy good food and wine. Table 514 is one of the special places to which they have repeatedly returned to quietly celebrate life, together.

On this particular night, the waiter delivers an enormous sterling container to the man and woman who sit across from one another on the booth's dark leather seats. The silver bowl, heaped to overflowing with cold lobster, crab, and shrimp, is more than enough for two people to share. To an observer, this might look like a typical dinner date. On closer inspection, though, one would see that this meal shared is a joyous observance. It is a discreet declaration of faith, hope, and love. It is a bittersweet memory that will linger in the heart and mind of a husband who has adored and loved without condition his bride of forty-six years. The seeming frailty of the strikingly beautiful woman disguises the fortitude of her spirit. The friendship, the kind of time- and trial-tested love that's unspoken between them, transcends the words that are now so difficult to exchange.

The scene is but a page in the real-life love story of Steve and Becky Schenck, that has spanned nearly half a century. While it foreshadows the narrative's imminent conclusion, it is, indeed, a celebration of both the moment itself and also all of those that have preceded it.

The serenity of this moment stands in contrast to some of the stressful circumstances the couple has faced over the past ten years. In August of 2006, Steve and Becky faced the crisis of a lifetime, when their entire future changed over the course of just a few short hours.

Table 514 at Ruth's Chris Steakhouse became a place of special significance for the Schencks. Becky and Steve (right) enjoyed dinner at the familiar spot with their son-in-law, Ben Garvin, and daughter, Julie Garvin (left), in March 2016.

CHAPTER 2
Something is Very Wrong

It was a hot, summer day at the community pool. Jim, the Schencks' oldest son, had brought the grandchildren for a swim.

Becky dipped her feet into the cool water. Something went wrong. A strange, out-of-body experience, like a wave of confusion, came over her.

"Grandma, Grandma, look at me, Grandma!" Granddaughter Olivia was twirling in the water. "Atta girl, Olivia!" Steve said.

Becky opened her mouth, to tell Olivia how wonderful she was. But her words were lost. She was unable to speak.

Becky looked around, alarmed. What was happening? Everyone else continued playing in the water, but for Becky, time stopped. Then, as suddenly as the terrifying episode began, it ended. Her voice returned.

Becky immediately told her family what she had experienced. "It's probably just the heat, Mom. It's ninety-five degrees and the humidity is unbearable," said Jim. "You're probably dehydrated, or maybe you had a little heat stroke."

The incident at the pool rattled Becky. She told her friends and they, too, brushed it off as a minor heat stroke. She knew that what she had experienced at the pool was something else. Then, three weeks later, the incident repeated itself.

Becky was cooking dinner and again felt the strange, out-of-body sensation. Not being one to complain, she didn't mention it to Steve or her daughter, Julie. Later in the evening, as Steve and Becky were going to bed, Becky turned to tell Steve something, and again, her words were stuck. She managed to say, "Something's really wrong." It was the onset of a seizure. Becky was frightened.

Steve was frightened, too, but he remained composed and said, "We're going for a ride, Becky." He sped to Community North Hospital's emergency room, pulled up to the entrance, and helped Becky out of the car. An attendant approached him. "Sir," he said, "you've entered the wrong way. You're going to have to move your car."

"My wife is having a stroke," said Steve. The attendant immediately got a wheelchair and wheeled Becky into the hospital. In the examination room, another seizure began.

Forces beyond her control suddenly seized and violently jerked Becky's body. She grunted and moaned. She drooled and bit her tongue. Steve watched in horror, unable to calm her or make the grand mal seizure stop.

Nurses lifted her small body into the bed and rolled Becky onto her side. They gave her Dilantin®, an anti-seizure medication. All they could do was wait for the seizure to run its course. Steve had never seen this happen to anyone, let alone his wife.

He sat on the edge of the bed and held Becky, while the tremors eventually subsided. "What's going on, Red?" he wondered, as he smoothed her auburn hair and brushed his finger across her cheek. "What's going on?" Steve and Becky had never encountered anything quite like this before. They would have to draw on the strength of God and each other in the crisis they now faced. They had developed this kind of reliance early on in their relationship. The strength they now drew upon had been forged over thirty-six years prior, when they weathered other painful, difficult circumstances together.

CHAPTER 3

Young Love

The year was 1969. The Beatles had just released *Abbey Road*. Neil Armstrong made history by landing on the moon. Richard Nixon was withdrawing troops from Vietnam and ABC introduced a new sitcom called *The Brady Bunch*. At the Kroger grocery store in Evansville, Indiana, Steve Schenck was working his way through college by managing the store's produce department.

On a warm fall afternoon, sixteen-year-old Becky Burk accompanied her mother on a quick stop at Kroger for a few groceries. Steve immediately noticed the vivacious teenager with beautiful auburn hair and big brown eyes. As he rang up Mrs. Burk's grocery order, he exchanged glances and a few words with Becky. He smelled of fresh produce. He made Becky smile. She liked him. He liked her. It was as simple as that.

Too bashful to ask her out on a date, Steve invited Becky and her friend, Phyllis, to join him and his friend at a high school football game. She accepted the invitation. Steve quickly discovered Becky's fun-loving nature, infectious sense of humor, and irresistible charm. As the game ended, he mustered up the courage to ask for her phone number. Having no paper or pen, he wrote the numbers "426-2362" into the dust of his 1965 red Plymouth.

The two began to date often, but knowing how different their families' religious traditions were, they kept their courtship a secret. Becky was the middle child in a strict Baptist family of five. Her grandfather was a minister. Steve was the fourth child in a Catholic family of seven. Their families' theological differences mattered little to Steve and Becky, who both believed in and loved God.

Their love for one another quickly grew. After a few months of dating, Becky discovered that she was pregnant, and Steve asked for her hand in marriage.

Becky's family was shocked and disappointed by the news. The job of planning the wedding was tense and difficult. A Catholic wedding Mass was out of the question for the Burks, and getting married in a Baptist church was not an acceptable option for the Schencks. The Schencks' priest and the Burks' minister even met to try to find a solution.

The differences in their families' theology and religious traditions didn't faze Steve and Becky. They shared a common faith in God that transcended their church affiliation, and a faith in each other and the relationship that God had given them. They decided to get married by the Justice of the Peace on January 10, 1970, three months after their first date. They celebrated after the wedding with both families, eating cake at the Burks' house and attending a party at the Schencks' home. They were happy and madly in love. Almost two weeks later, Becky celebrated her seventeenth birthday.

Steve graduated from what is now the University of Southern Indiana and began working at a public accounting firm in Evansville. With a checkbook balance of $250, the newlywed couple rented their first home.

By September, Becky was eight months pregnant. Steve had his wisdom teeth removed, and after the routine surgery, Becky drove to pick up his pain medication. As she pulled out from the pharmacy, an oncoming car hit the red Plymouth on the driver's side. The impact was powerful, and though Becky survived, Gina, their unborn child, did not. It was a heart-wrenching loss for the young couple. In their sorrow, they drew even closer together. Becky became pregnant for a second time, with their son, Jim. They experienced the joy of his birth in 1972.

CHAPTER 4

We Are Family

Within a couple of years, Steve and Becky moved to Lafayette, Indiana, where Steve had accepted an accounting position with National Homes. In 1973, he accepted a position in the internal audit department at Indiana National Bank, in Indianapolis. It was a new place and an exciting, new beginning for them.

The Schencks' second son, Scott, was born in 1975, and Andy in 1978. Becky was a natural in her role as a stay-at-home mom. She loved children. Having three boys was at times a handful, but she managed it all with grace and love. She was fair, but also strict enough to earn the title "cop" from her sons.

With the birth of daughter, Julie, in 1982, Becky was a very busy young mom. Steve recalls coming home to find her cooking chicken and french fries in the Fry Daddy and setting the dinner table, all with baby Julie in the crux of her arm.

Over the years, the family created great memories together. Christmas was Becky's favorite holiday, and she made it a special time for her family. Every year, she decorated the house with candles, garland, and an impressively decorated tree. She and Steve showered the kids with the latest toys and clothing. In the summers, they vacationed near Myrtle Beach, South Carolina.

As the children grew, both Steve and Becky were actively involved in their activities. Steve helped out with Little League. Becky joined the Parent-Teacher Organization and frequently volunteered at the school. Steve and Becky co-chaired a Drug-Free School Zone campaign for the Lawrence Township schools, and in 1992, they received the Superintendent's Award for their involvement in raising awareness and developing corporate sponsorship. As the children entered middle school and high school, Becky loved, protected, and stayed involved with each of her children as they each navigated the difficult years of being a teenager.

Around this time, Steve developed a friendship with Dr. Tim Kelly, who was then medical director at Fairbanks addiction treatment center. Steve later joined the organization's board of directors and eventually became its chairman. He had no idea then how invaluable this friendship would later become.

CHAPTER 5

Building a Legacy with Love for the Community

Steve and Becky both shared a deep passion for the Indianapolis community, and they were active participants in it, both as a couple and as individuals. In 2002, they received the Outstanding Volunteer Fundraisers Award from the Indiana Chapter of the Association of Fundraising Professionals for their involvement.

Steve was a busy executive who lent his time and expertise to many organizations, serving on the board of directors for the United Way of Central Indiana, the Indianapolis Zoo, the Indianapolis Chamber of Commerce, the Indiana Chamber Committee for Responsive Government, Fairbanks, and the advisory board for Indiana University Kelley School of Business. He also was involved with the Boy Scouts Crossroads of America Counsel of Central Indiana, the Indiana CPA Society, and the American Institute of CPAs. In 2008, Governor Mitch Daniels appointed him as a member of the University of Southern Indiana Trustees. He received numerous awards for his volunteer work, including the Distinguished Citizen Award from the Multiple Sclerosis Society and the Outstanding Philanthropy Award from the

Association of Fundraising Professionals. "Becky was right there with him," says the Schencks' friend, Mary Beth Oakes. "She recognized all of his talent and potential. She was a great partner. She supported him in every endeavor."

In 1999, Steve joined the board of directors of the 500 Festival, a non-profit organization that plans civic events on the days leading up to the Indianapolis 500. He and Becky worked together to help plan and execute these events for six years. They spent long hours with the other couples that were involved with the Festival. In the process, they developed close friendships with Mary Beth and Dick Oakes, Bellinda and Scott Blumenthal, and John and Cindy Barnes. The four couples socialized together so often that they eventually coined themselves "The Crazy Eight." They traveled, dined, and volunteered together. "I think we were so lucky with Steve and Becky. It was very special," shares

The Schencks and their friends dubbed themselves the "Crazy Eight." From left to right are: Bellinda and Scott Blumenthal, Mary Beth and Dick Oakes, Becky and Steve, and Cynde and John Barnes.

Mary Beth. "It's hard to find couples friends. To me, that was really unique. You go through life, and it's hard to find another couple you really like doing things with. That's how we felt about Steve and Becky. We loved them."

Becky contributed her own high energy and enthusiasm to many organizations, as well. The Indianapolis Zoo was one of her favorite causes and the annual Zoobilation one of her favorite events. She was a member of the Indianapolis Zoo Guild and became the zoo's Nussbaum Committee Chair in 2003. "Becky was a charismatic leader. No one will ever forget her legacy," says Mary Beth.

Becky also enjoyed serving on the advisory board for *Indianapolis Woman* magazine and the board of directors for the Indianapolis Library Foundation. She was a member of the Hoosier Alliance Against Drugs and numerous giving societies.

In 2004, Becky's neighbor and long-time friend, Beth O'Neil, invited her to join the board of directors for the Christamore House Guild, a non-profit organization that provides early childhood education, after-school programming, senior citizen services, preventative services, and employment assistance to the residents of the near west side of Indianapolis. In a 2008 *Indianapolis Star* interview, Becky recalled her friend's invitation. Reporter Susan Guyett wrote: "Schenck, the mother of four, thought she was too busy to get involved with hands-on volunteering. She still remembers calling O'Neil after her first day working at the preschool. 'I am so mad I didn't do this sooner,' she told her. 'It was the best thing I've ever done in my life,' she said of her years with Christamore House" (*Indianapolis Star*, November 16, 2008).

"Becky was a charismatic leader. No one will ever forget her legacy."

Mary Beth Oakes

Becky was extremely committed to this cause. During the fifteen years of her involvement as a guild member and volunteer, she brought fresh ideas to the table and worked ceaselessly to execute her plans. She loved being around the children and helping to provide them with a solid education.

In her third year with the Christamore House, she became the Guild President. She served meals to the neighbors in the rough streets of Haughville. Her favorite work was directly helping others, and she gave selflessly of her time and energy.

Becky looked forward most to preparing the Christamore House for the Christmas season. Just as she had done with her own family, Becky took Christmas to a whole new level, ensuring that the children of the Christamore House had a festive and memorable holiday. She spent weeks planning, decorating, and shopping. She asked store managers all over the city if they would donate gifts to the Christamore House children. She personally chose a gift for every child.

The Christamore House expressed its gratitude for Becky's service and generosity in 2007, when it renamed its Early Childhood Education Center the Becky Schenck Early Childhood Education Center. The *Indianapolis Star* reported the details of the announcement. Guyett wrote:

"The choice of music could not have been more perfect when students at Christamore House broke into 'Twinkle, Twinkle Little Star' in honor of Becky Schenck.

Schenck, a longtime volunteer and Christamore House supporter, is little, as in petite. Anyone who has ever spent time with her knows she's a star. But during the past year, after doctors discovered she had a malignant brain tumor, she's shown the world the meaning of strength and courage. She's still undergoing treatment.

Christamore House officials renamed the Early Childhood Education Center in her honor Wednesday with a crowd of friends, fans, and family on hand to celebrate the recognition.

'Through the years, Becky has spent hundreds of volunteer hours in support of the Christamore House, and the organization felt it was only fitting to recognize such a caring and compassionate community leader,' friend Mary Beth Oakes said.

Olgen Williams, executive director of Christamore House, told the gathering that Schenck was influential in expanding the early education program from a half day to a full day and getting the playground built. She also had a personal impact on the children whose lives she touched, Oakes said.

Her colleagues from the Indianapolis-Marion County Public Library Foundation board were on hand, as were officials of the Indianapolis Zoo. Schenck and her husband, Steve Schenck, chief executive of Midwest operations for Regions Bank, have supported the zoo for many years" (*Indianapolis Star*, March 15, 2007).

Becky left a legacy at the Christamore House. She and Steve are pictured here, with children at the Becky Schenck Early Childhood Education Center and with Cynthia James, director of the Christamore House Early Childhood Development Center (left) and writer Erin Sheets (right).

CHAPTER 6
A Grim Diagnosis

On the day of Becky's first seizure, in 2006, a computed tomography (CT) scan revealed a tumor in her brain. The doctors assumed it to be benign, but they scheduled a magnetic resonance imaging (MRI), to be sure. The family waited in the hospital lounge for hours. Steve called friends and extended family members, sharing the news and asking for their prayers. Some of their closest friends came to the hospital to offer their love and support. Their son, Andy, was in Florida, and booked the next flight home when he received his dad's urgent call.

Steve also contacted his long-time friend, Dr. Kelly, with Community Health Network. When he arrived, he reviewed the MRI and the doctor's notes. "It's high-grade glioblastoma," he informed Steve.

"What does it mean?" asked Steve. He had never heard the word "glioblastoma" before. "It means it's not good," Dr. Kelly replied.

As the two men approached the elevator, the door opened, and there was Andy, who had just arrived from Florida. Steve smiled at him and tried to be his strong, positive self. They stepped into the elevator and, as soon as the doors shut, Steve broke down with emotion. It was the first time Andy had ever seen his father cry.

Three days after she had been admitted to the hospital, the family gathered around Becky. The doctor confirmed that she had advanced-stage glioblastoma multiforme (GBM), a rare, very aggressive, and deadly form of brain cancer. He explained that GBM tumors arise from astrocytes, the star-shaped cells that make up the brain's supportive tissue.

Becky immediately wanted to know her prognosis. "We estimate that you have a year to fifteen months," the doctor told her. The family was stunned.

"It was an awful feeling," Becky remembers. "I wanted to know how long I had to live. All of a sudden, my life wasn't going to be as long as I thought. I wasn't going to have as much time with my kids and grandkids." She later recalled her memories of that day, in a 2012 United Way video. "I remember that day," she said. "I cried and I cried."[1] Their son, Andy, recalls, "It came out of nowhere; my mom has always been healthy. It was definitely a mind-numbing experience. When you are first diagnosed and they give you a death sentence, a year to live, that's hard to swallow. The initial diagnosis hit me very hard. You never expect something like this is going to happen to your family."

Becky thought about her hopes and dreams for the future — to see her children get married and have children, to see her future grandchildren, to retire and grow old with Steve. The future she and Steve had dreamed about was gone.

Glioblastoma Multiforme (GBM) at a Glance

- The American Brain Tumor Association (ABTA) reports that there currently are nearly 700,000 people in the U.S. living with a primary brain and central nervous system tumor. An estimated 12,120 new cases of glioblastoma are predicted in 2016.[2]

- The overall five-year survival rate for GBM remains less than 5 percent.[3]

- GBM has an incidence of two to three per 100,000 adults per year, and accounts for 52 percent of all primary brain tumors. Overall, GBM accounts for about 17 percent of all tumors of the brain.[4] The National Cancer Institute estimates 23,770 new cases of brain and other nervous system cancer in 2016.

CHAPTER 7
Exploring Options and Fighting Back

Becky's diagnosis came as a shock to everyone. "Nothing can prepare you for news like that," says Steve. "Our lives changed in an instant." The couple's first response was to turn to their faith. "We knew God, and our relationship with Him was so important to us," says Steve. "We knew that in that moment, we needed to turn our lives and this new situation over to His care." They gathered the family together and committed to one another that faith, family, and friends would continue to guide everything they did. Turning to their faith and family values was a natural response for the Schencks. Margaretta Page, R.N. at University of California San Francisco and co-author of *Transitions in Care for Patients with Brain Tumors: Palliative and Hospice Care* (2014, The Regents of the University of California), says that this kind of focus is critical in the face of a brain cancer diagnosis. "It is important for doctors

> **"I am not giving up. That is just me, I am a go-getter and I am not going to give up."**
> Becky Schenck, with Anne Marie Tiernon, Indianapolis NBC affiliate, WTHR-TV

and families to talk with patients about their values and what is important to them so that care can be tailored with that in mind," she says.

Despite the grim prognosis, Becky was immediately determined to fight her newly diagnosed disease. It never crossed her nor Steve's minds to do anything else. In an interview with Indianapolis NBC affiliate WTHR-TV, she shared her thoughts with reporter, Anne Marie Tiernon. She expressed her attitude toward the deadly disease that holds no cure. "I am not giving up. That is just me, I am a go-getter and I am not going to give up. I will fight until I die," she said. [6] Her daughter, Julie, told *Indianapolis Woman*, "The first words out of her mouth were, 'I am going to fight this, and I am going to beat it.'"[7]

Steve and Becky called their friends, the Oakes, to tell them the grim news. "It seemed surreal," remembers Mary Beth. "It didn't seem possible. I remember thinking, 'What a remarkable person she is; how brave.' So many people would have given up and gotten so discouraged that they couldn't function. But that's not Becky." Bellinda Blumenthal agrees. "Becky is amazing. She has been a hero in the face of adversity. What an example she is."

The only question in Steve and Becky's minds now was how to best fight the cancer. Steve searched the internet, eager to learn more about the disease that had thrust its way into their working vocabulary. Glioblastoma multiforme (GBM), he learned, was the worst possible scenario.

The rare form of cancer resides in the body's most complex and fundamental organ, the brain. While scientists are making rapid discoveries about this organ, much remains unknown. GBM's insidious, finger-like projections make it essentially impossible for doctors to fully remove. By the time a patient exhibits GBM symptoms, which can include headaches, nausea, vomiting, and seizures, the tumor may have already become late-stage cancer. This is why many patients with GBM do not live beyond a year; some don't make it past three months. There was no cure for the disease; only treatments that might prolong Becky's life for a short time, and perhaps at a great detriment to the quality of her life.

Steve looked for online or other resources that might help them navigate the difficult decisions they faced about Becky's course of treatment. This was completely unknown territory for both of them.

According to Page, it's important, after a brain cancer diagnosis, that someone close to the patient steps into the role of caregiver. "Initially, there is a need for information. The patient is often recovering from brain surgery and caregivers often play a big role in helping to gather the information," she says. "The caregiver may process fully or help a patient understand what treatments are being recommended by the doctor. Caregivers are often the conduit of information and communicators with the health team about appointments, symptoms, medications, etc. As the illness progresses, caregivers become the main contact between patient and health care team." The caregiver's role is crucial at each step of the way.

"Caregivers have to walk a fine line, allowing for patient independence, but with an awareness that the brain tumor can cause problems with memory and judgment. They need to support the patient, without taking over. This can be challenging at times," Page explains.

The Schencks' friend, Tim Kelly, M.D., Community Health Network, was a tremendous source of help and support.

The early days after Becky's diagnosis were scary and sometimes confusing. She and Steve talked, prayed for guidance and clear direction, and began to explore their options. One of the Schencks' potential resources came through their friend, Dr. Kelly, who fully understood the gravity of the situation they were facing. Dr. Kelly and Dr. Jennifer Morgan, an oncologist with IU Health, researched several clinical trials that were being conducted, using experimental cancer medications. A trial drug could potentially give Becky a chance to fight back at the cancer and, most importantly, offer her and her family hope.

In the meantime, Becky needed both chemotherapy and immediate surgery, to remove as much of the tumor as possible. It would be a difficult surgery, indeed, because the tumor resided in the left temporal lobe of her brain. This is a particularly high-risk area because the left temporal lobe is responsible for language processing, speech, and memory. The Schencks needed a highly skilled and experienced neurosurgeon who would take Becky's case.

They first approached a leading group of neurosurgeons in Indiana to look at Becky's MRI and make recommendations. The first doctor told them that the tumor's location would make surgery extremely difficult. He consulted a fellow neurosurgeon who specialized in brain mapping, a technique that creates a three-dimensional atlas of the brain in microscopic detail. He agreed with his colleague's conclusion. This kind of surgery was out of his realm, but he knew who could handle precisely the type of procedure that Becky needed. "Dr. Mitch Berger practices in San Francisco," he told the Schencks. "He is a busy man; he's *the* man." Dr. Berger is chair of the neurological surgery department at the UCSF and director of the university's Brain Tumor Research Center. He also has pioneered brain mapping techniques used to identify speech, motor, and sensory areas that should be avoided during surgery. "Mapping is a big deal," Steve says. "We knew that we needed to get the guy who is the best at this." They called and left a message for Dr. Berger and waited to hear back. It was a long week. They didn't know it, but Dr. Berger was out of the country and hadn't received their message.

Brain Mapping[5]

- The brain is the most complicated organ in our body. Every area has a specific function that controls everything that we do. For years, doctors have had a rough map of the brain, but never to the degree that they could operate and know for sure how to avoid every critical portion, since each person's brain is unique, causing variations in the map. This fact, combined with the sheer complexity of the brain, has challenged neurosurgeons for years.

- Through groundbreaking research pioneered at UCSF, an advanced brain mapping technique has enabled doctors to remove as much of a brain tumor as possible, while minimizing the impact on the crucial areas of the brain that control movement, speech, and the senses.

- By using three-dimensional imaging technology to operate on the brain, surgeons can accurately target their dissection down to the smallest degree. The goal is to remove all or most of the tumor without producing any permanent neurological deficit in the patient.

Minimizing Impact on Healthy Tissue:

  - During the surgery, the patient is awake for a portion of the surgical procedure to help surgeons with an understanding of the functional areas of the brain near the tumor. This allows doctors to map out their path to a successful surgery, while minimizing impact on healthy, vital tissue.

  - The patient is allowed to return to consciousness after the brain has been exposed, and then interacts with the team as they stimulate areas of the brain near the tumor.

  - For example, the neurosurgeon may stimulate the brain where it controls feelings in the mouth and gums, causing the patient to experience tingling or tongue twitching. Language testing is also performed.

  - Once the areas of the eloquent cortex have been identified, the patient is put back under general anesthesia and the surgery is completed.

  - Brain mapping is also being used to treat other diseases such as epilepsy.

Caregiving Following a Diagnosis

The diagnosis of a life-threatening disease is a crisis that can be overwhelming, frightening, and confusing for a patient and their family. Establishing a family member, friend, or other person as a caregiver is an important step to take in the difficult days that follow diagnosis. Steve offers these suggestions to caregivers at this stage in the journey:

- Look for *Orientation to Caregiving: A Handbook for Family Caregivers of Patients with Brain Tumors*, a free, online resource from UCSF. It contains all kinds of practical advice for caregivers and information for those who are dealing with brain cancer. The electronic publication can be found at https://www.ucsfhealth.org/pdf/ucsf_caregiver_handbook.pdf.

- Become your loved one's advocate in starting the quest for the best course of disease treatment.

- Receiving a diagnosis is incredibly stressful and overwhelming. The patient and family are often in a state of shock at a time when they are receiving important information. Taking notes or even recording conversations with the doctor gives you an opportunity to review the information later, when your thinking is clearer.

- Don't be afraid to ask lots of questions about the disease, so that you understand exactly what you are dealing with.

- After you receive the diagnosis and prognosis, do some online research to broaden your understanding about the disease. As you look for information, though, avoid reading the heart-wrenching stories or worst-case scenarios that are posted. Personal accounts aren't always accurate and they can foster your worst fears.

- Ask lots of questions about all available treatment options. Don't automatically take the first recommended course of action, until you understand all of your alternatives.

- Talk to doctors about clinical trials that are being conducted with experimental treatments for the disease your loved one is facing. These research studies may offer a source of hope.

- Draw on friends and family who have medical experience or who might have contacts in the medical arena. They might be able to offer ideas or resources beyond your scope of knowledge.

CHAPTER 8

Assembling a Medical "Dream Team"

While Steve and Becky were waiting to hear back from Dr. Berger at UCSF, a doctor from IU Health reached out to them, to see if they wanted a second opinion. Eager for answers, Steve and Becky scheduled an appointment with him. The doctor said, "You know Becky, I'm more worried about the quality of your life than the quantity of your life. I just don't think you need to go to San Francisco." He went on, "My brother died recently of cancer. He was fifty-five [Becky's age at the time]. You need to consider the quality of the time you have left." It was a lot for Steve and Becky to think about. They wanted Becky to have as many quality days as possible, but they desperately wanted to fight the disease. Sitting back without taking action just wasn't their style.

A few days later, Steve received a phone call. "Steve, this is Dr. Mitch Berger." Steve felt a rise of hope. "I've seen your wife's scans." Dr. Berger took a long pause. "I think I can help. The only problem is, I don't know when I can do it." His schedule was so full that he might not be able to take on Becky's case. Steve fought his feelings of discouragement. Then Dr. Berger said, "I'm going to be in Indianapolis for a talk and may be able to do it while I'm in town. I'll have to get back to you and let you know."

Becky and Steve spent another couple of days praying and waiting for the call and the hope it promised. Finally, Dr. Berger called and said, "I've decided that I can't do it in Indianapolis. I really need my team for this. Can you fly in to San Francisco next Wednesday?" Steve and Becky immediately booked a flight.

The UCSF Neuro-Oncology team played a big role in Becky's treatment. Pictured here (left to right) are: Nicholas Bukowski, M.D., Mitch Berger, M.D., and Director of Neuro-Oncology, Susan Chang, M.D. (Photo courtesy of UCSF and John Branscombe, photographer)

Becky would also require an oncologist close to home, for chemotherapy and radiation. Dr. Kelly highly recommended Dr. Jennifer Morgan at IU Health, who had helped them identify potential clinical trial options. Dr. Kelly advised the Schencks, "You've got to go with her. She's not only highly competent, she's nurturing, too. When it comes to bedside manner, nobody beats Jennifer." The Schencks made an appointment to meet Dr. Morgan as soon as they returned to Indiana after the surgery.

The Schencks began to weigh their treatment options, including the possibility of a clinical trial. Steve asked the doctors, "How do we choose a course of treatment that will ensure her the most quality days? What if, with surgery and a clinical trial, she could have another ten years? There's no way of knowing what will come of the treatments, but we at least need to try." Becky was willing to risk the unknown outcome of a clinical trial, with the hope that it might give her more time with her family and friends. The answer was becoming clearer.

One of the trials they learned about was one being conducted by Eli Lilly and Co., an Indianapolis-based pharmaceutical manufacturer. It was exciting for Steve and Becky to think that the trial drug had been developed in the heart of the community that they loved so much. Dr. Berger and UCSF neuro-oncologist Dr. Nicholas Butowski were administering Lilly's phase I clinical trial. Dr. Butowski specializes in brain tumors, neuro-imaging, cognitive and rehabilitative neurology, and complementary therapy. Steve did his homework, and found that both men had extensive curriculum vitae, full of impressive degrees, publications, awards, and board appointments.

With doctors of this caliber, the choice to join the Lilly trial seemed clear. Dr. Kelly and Dr. Morgan, with the support of Sam Odle, the former chief operating officer of IU Health and chief executive officer of Methodist Hospital and University Hospital, worked together to help Becky with choosing the UCSF clinical trial. But there was a slight catch. The trial stipulated that Dr. Butowski's team administer the trial drug. Even though Lilly is located in Indianapolis, just thirty minutes from the Schencks' home in the suburbs, participation in the clinical trial mandated monthly trips across the country, to San Francisco. Steve and Becky were fortunate to be able to accommodate the financial commitment these multiple trips would require. They were more than willing to travel to UCSF's Department of Neurological Surgery, if it meant having these two accomplished doctors on their side.

All of the pieces had fallen into place. Steve and Becky's prayers were being answered. They found relief in having made the decision to move forward with the clinical trial. Thanks to Dr. Kelly's help in connecting them to valuable resources, they had their "Dream Team" of trusted doctors assembled.

A few nights before flying to California for surgery, friends Mary Beth and Dick Oakes invited Steve and Becky over for dinner. They laughed and shared stories. Becky hugged Mary Beth and said, "I'm gonna beat this." She was sure of it.

Financial Assistance Resources

Even for those who have insurance coverage, cancer treatment can be expensive. According to http://www.giveforward.com, a 2011 study by Duke University showed that the average cancer patient in the US pays over $8,500 a year in out-of-pocket medical expenses not covered by insurance.[8]

Sometimes, patients rule out treatment options that are cost-prohibitive. Before making a decision, check out the many organizations that offer financial help for treatment-related expenses. Here are a few resources to explore:

- Cancer Financial Assistance Coalition (http://www.cancerfac.org)
- CancerCare (http://www.cancercarecopay.org)
- Health Well Foundation (http://www.healthwellfoundation.org)
- Leukemia & Lymphoma Society (http://www.lls.org/financial-support)
- The C.H.A.I.N. Fund (http://www.thechainfund.com)
- The American Cancer Society (http://www.cancer.org)
- Local agencies, such as Catholic Charities, Jewish Social Services, the Lions Club, Lutheran Social Services, and the Salvation Army
- Healthcare Hospitality Network (http://www.hhnetwork.org)
- The Angel Bus (http://www.angel-bus.org)
- Air Charity Network (http://www.aircharitynetwork.org)
- The Air Care Alliance (http://www.aircareall.org)
- National Patient Travel Center (http://www.patienttravel.org)
- Corporate Angel Network (http://www.corpangelnetwork.org)
- Patient Airlift Services (http://www.palservices.org)
- Mercy Medical Airlift (http://www.mercymedical.org)

CHAPTER 9
Surgery in San Francisco

Steve and Becky landed in San Francisco in September of 2006 and went directly to their first appointment for an updated MRI. They also met with a neurologist who would prepare Becky for the brain mapping by asking her a series of questions that would be repeated during the surgery.

The next morning, the couple arrived at the hospital at seven o'clock. Anxiety was high, and magazines were an ineffective distraction from what was to come.

Finally, it was time for surgery. With Becky safely sedated, the neurosurgeon skillfully removed a tumorous piece of tissue from Becky's brain and exposed the left temporal lobe.

The anesthesiologist woke her up temporarily so that she could respond to a series of questions. Her responses would enable the surgeon to map out the areas that could be cut and the areas to avoid. The goal was to remove as much of the tumor as possible, without affecting areas that would affect Becky's ability to speak and process language.

Becky opened her eyes and looked around the room. "Everyone around me was dressed in blue scrubs," she remembers, "and it was all so sterile. You can't feel pain. When I woke up, I could see them all there, in their surgical gowns. I felt like I was asleep, but I remember it vividly. Someone showed me the pictures and said that it was time to tell them what I see. They put letters on different parts of the brain to say that that area has been cleared. The cards they show you are things like squirrels and other objects."

Dr. Berger began a series of questions:

"Becky, what do you paint with?"

"A paintbrush."

"What do you sleep on?"

"A bed."

"What are the days of the week?"

Becky hesitated, and the surgeon placed a marker directly on her brain. With the brain mapping complete, the anesthesiologist restored Becky's full sedation, so that Dr. Berger could skillfully remove as much of her tumor as possible. Her skull was refastened with plates and screws. The entire procedure lasted over eight hours. Following the surgery, the doctors confirmed Becky's GBM as being stage-four cancer; the most advanced stage of the disease. Only time would tell how long she had left.

Upon waking from the anesthesia, Becky's memory and speech were affected; a normal symptom after such a traumatic surgery. This symptom, called aphasia, is common in brain cancer patients, with tumors in the left temporal lobe.

At one point, while she was in the intensive care unit, Becky's blood pressure dropped so low that it triggered the alarms on her monitors. Nurses came running to hook her up to intravenous fluids. Steve's heart was in his throat, trying not to imagine the worst. The nurses quickly stabilized Becky's blood pressure, and after that her recovery went smoothly and remarkably well. After twenty-four hours, Becky began to see some improvement, but she still had trouble with her speech.

Becky stayed in the ICU for only one day. Within four days, she was discharged from the hospital. She left, dressed beautifully, with her shaven head wrapped in a silk scarf covering the bandages that protected the sixty-eight staples from surgery.

Dr. Kelly called Steve every single day for ninety days after Becky's surgery, to see how she was doing. On only the fifth night after Becky's surgery, Steve answered the daily call and told his friend, "Well, Tim, I'm at dinner right now, at a steakhouse near the hotel."

Dr. Kelly was a bit perplexed. "At a steakhouse? Did you leave Becky at the hotel to rest?" he asked.

"No, she's sitting right here, next to me, eating a steak!" Steve replied.

Becky had decided that brain surgery wasn't going to stop her from enjoying a dinner out with her husband. On this first of many future trips to San Francisco, she was determined to make the most of the time together.

After ten days of recuperation, Steve and Becky boarded a plane back to Indianapolis. Traveling across the country after surgery was difficult, but Steve and Becky were happy.

CHAPTER 10
Friends Express Their Love

With Becky's surgery behind them, the Schencks returned to their home in Fishers, Indiana. As Steve pulled into the driveway, he noticed a blue cooler on the front steps. Upon opening it, he and Becky discovered that their friend, Beth O'Neil, had arranged for their friends and neighbors to take turns preparing meals for them. "I admired her determination, her bravery, and her faith," says Beth. "So many people wanted to help." Friends looked for ways to reach out to Steve and Becky, who had devoted their lives to giving to family and many other organizations. This time, it was their turn to receive. In situations like these, said their friend, Bellinda, "You don't ask what you can do, just do. It shows you care."

The Schencks' friends delivered meals to the family, in a blue cooler on the front porch of their home (Photo courtesy of *Indianapolis Woman* and PULSPhotography).

Friends also helped by driving Becky to her medical appointments so that Steve could continue to work. Their friends were always there for them, helping them carry on as normal a life as possible, given the circumstances. "It was almost like we were waiting for Becky to ask 'Why me?' or 'This is so awful and so hard,'" says her friend, Mary Beth. "But she never talked like that. She always looked at the next step and how she was going to move forward."

> **"She always looked at the next step and how she was going to move forward."**
>
> Mary Beth Oakes

For the most part, Steve and Becky were able to carry on as they had before Becky's diagnosis. Fewer than two weeks after surgery, they had dinner with their friends, the Oakes. Becky looked beautiful, in a teal dress and a scarf tied around her head. "Who does that?" Mary Beth says, lightheartedly. "Who has brain surgery, gets dressed up, and goes out to dinner so quickly afterwards? That night, we were celebrating her."

CHAPTER 11
Hugs, Radiation, and Chemotherapy

Following Becky's surgery, it was time for Steve and Becky to finally meet Dr. Morgan in person. She had been instrumental in assisting with Becky's clinical trial application, and Steve had been emailing her regularly. They drove to Dr. Morgan's office, which was located in a small office park on the north side of Fishers, not far from the Schencks' home.

Dr. Morgan greeted them warmly, then perched on a small stool. "It's so nice to finally meet you," she said. Becky and Steve immediately felt safe and hopeful in her presence. She was brilliant and compassionate.

Jennifer Morgan, M.D., IU Health, provided oncology care for Becky in Indianapolis (photo courtesy of IU Health).

Dr. Morgan prescribed Temodar®, a chemotherapy drug for GBM, as well as radiation treatments. Temodar made a potential twelve- to fifteen-month life expectancy possible. The medication attacks the remaining cancer cells in the brain, but has some serious side effects, including fatigue, loss of appetite, and nausea.

Temodar would be given daily for five consecutive days, followed by a twenty-three-day break, in four-week cycles. Becky also took a daily dose of the Lilly trial drug, a form of chemotherapy which they hoped would prevent the cancer from growing.

Every appointment with Dr. Morgan began and ended with a hug. This simple act made a huge difference in Becky's treatment. Dr. Morgan understood that fighting cancer is about more than stopping the growth of malignant cells; it's also about showing care and compassion to patients and their families. She knew about the emotions that accompany a diagnosis like GBM. "The original prognosis and all the stress and anxiety that comes into the equation is almost like Post Traumatic Stress Disorder (PTSD)," explains Dr. Morgan. "Every step of the way, there's depression and anxiety. The patient recovers, then waits for the next MRI thinking, 'I made it this time,' but the anxiety and depression builds up for the next MRI."

Becky was scheduled for external beam radiation therapy, to eradicate any parts of the cancer that were not removed through surgery or destroyed by chemotherapy. A technician made a fitted mask of Becky's face. It would ensure that the radiation struck only the area where Becky's cancer was, then exit back out of her body.

While the radiation itself is painless, the side effects can be difficult to manage. Becky was exhausted after her almost daily radiation treatment. No amount of rest satiated her fatigue. But she never complained. She was just thankful that she didn't experience the intense nausea, which is another common side effect of radiation.

Losing her hair was a difficult side effect of treatment, but Becky handled it with a positive attitude and with stylish scarves and wigs. She's pictured here with her granddaughters, Addison (left) and Olivia (right).

Losing her beautiful auburn hair was hard, at first. It was an important part of her femininity and style. But with Becky's characteristic sense of humor, she used the opportunity to get Steve to shave the mustache he had been sporting for the last thirty-five years. "I've lost my hair, so you can lose your mustache," she said. "At first, it bothered me a lot to go without a scarf or wig and to see those scars from the surgery," shared Becky in her interview with journalist Anne Ryder, in *Indianapolis Woman*. "It really bothered me. But I have to say, once I got used to no hair, I accepted it, and it wasn't a big deal anymore. I ordered maybe ten different wigs the first time. I used to never leave the house without looking good, without having my hair and makeup done. But knowing I only had twelve months, it suddenly become irrelevant."

CHAPTER 12

Life on Life's Terms

The chemotherapy drugs and radiation meant that Becky had some good days and some not-so-good days. On the good days, Becky's life was almost normal. She remained positive and upbeat.

Becky continued to pour her heart into her work with the Christamore House. The women from "The Crazy Eight" spent time together whenever they could. They had grown close to one another in the years prior to Becky's diagnosis, enjoying shopping trips together, to Chicago, New York, and Florida.

During this time, Becky was able to continue much of her social life. At a 2008 black tie conservation gala for the Indianapolis Zoo, she was thrilled when she and Steve were asked to help host one of her favorite television celebrities, Sam Waterston (star of the television show, *Law & Order*), for

Becky met her favorite actor, Sam Waterston, at a special event in 2008.

the evening. A photo from the event is one of the many framed memories that adorn Steve's home office. During that same year, Becky was well enough to fly down to Florida to surprise Mary Beth for her friend's fortieth birthday celebration.

The "Crazy Eight" threw a big birthday party for Becky, and also for their friend, Dick. They were surprised that she had the energy to celebrate, but she was there, in full strength. She looked incredible, and even blew out the candles on her birthday cake. "Our lives are so much better for having Becky as our friend. She's one of those kinds of people; having her as your friend makes your life better," says Mary Beth.

"Everything is a blessing. I mean everything."

Becky Schenck, in an interview with Indianapolis NBC affiliate, WTHR-TV

Becky stayed in close touch with her friends, never forgetting a birthday or anniversary. When Mary Beth's mother passed away, Mary Beth invited Becky to the funeral, but knowing Becky's condition, she didn't expect her to come. She was touched and surprised when Becky arrived at the funeral in support of her friend.

It was important to the Schencks' daughter, Julie, that her mom be part of her wedding. She and her fiancé, Ben, began to make plans. Becky helped Julie shop for her wedding dress, even though the short trips left her exhausted. She watched proudly as Steve walked their daughter down the aisle on August 9, 2008. Andy also married in 2008.

Becky fought hard to be part of these priceless family occasions. When Julie became pregnant, Becky took her shopping for baby clothes. On the day of that excursion, Julie remembers, Becky seemed to be her old self – bubbly, full of energy, and with an eye for style.

On most weekends, the Schencks' children and grandchildren came to the house to visit. Becky had always been a hands-on grandparent and she loved to be involved in each grandchild's life. Whenever she was able, she participated in outings and family gatherings that included them. As the kids grew, she and Steve attended their school and athletic functions, as often as possible.

Becky was grateful to be part of her grandchildren's lives (left to right): Addison, Evelyn, Olivia, Sam, Luke, Becky, Noah, Charlie (holding Graham).

Becky was blessed to be present for the births of all of her grandchildren: Addison, Evelyn, Olivia, Sam, Luke, Noah, Charlie, and Graham. In an interview with Anne Marie Tiernon of Indianapolis NBC affiliate WTHR-TV, Becky said, "Everything is a blessing. I mean everything. The children, I not only see three kids, I've seen seven kids grow up, which I never thought I would see."

However, on the not-so-good days, Becky spent a lot of time resting on the couch or in bed. She had to cut back significantly on activities she loved. Her balance was affected, which made it too difficult to ride a bike or go to the gym.

Becky's extreme fatigue made it difficult for her to continue B&B Enterprises, the Carlisle clothing business she loved and had started in 2003 with her friend, Bellinda. Becky's love for fashion and her savvy entrepreneurial skills had been a perfect combination for the company. "I jumped at the chance to work with Becky," remembers Bellinda. The women enjoyed sampling the new clothes and being privy to the latest fashions. They became prosperous business partners and even closer friends, and proudly spent all of their profits (and then some) on the clothing they loved. They often spent time together at the gym. Bellinda maintained the business for another year after Becky became ill, but eventually dissolved it. Without Becky, it just wasn't the same.

For the first two years of treatment, Steve and Becky made the monthly trips to San Francisco, so that Dr. Butowski's team could study the progress of the trial drug. In the process, Steve overcame his lifelong fear of flying on airplanes. He kept a positive attitude about the frequent travel. "As long as we're in the airplane seats, life is good," he said.

Becky also received an MRI once a month, to ensure that her condition was stable. "During that time, we looked at life differently," says Steve. "The radiation, the seizures that Becky had starting not long after the surgery, she had to take medicine for that. The traveling was hard. We'd leave early in the morning, be there for an afternoon appointment, go to dinner, then fly back the next morning. We just had to learn to sit back in the seat and relax."

Frequent and sudden seizures were one of the most difficult symptoms of her disease. Sometimes, they happened during the flights to San Francisco, thousands of feet in the air, causing flight attendants to want to make an emergency landing or get a doctor to help. On these occasions, Steve calmed them and explained that there was no reason for medical help, because there was nothing that could be done. He had to get a letter from the doctors in order for the airlines to allow them to fly.

Major occasions seemed to trigger the seizures, and given Steve and Becky's social life, the seizures happened frequently. But Becky didn't want to miss out on these gatherings, so she put on a brave face and continued going to events, even though it meant dealing with seizures in very public settings. Steve was there to support her and to help her leave the room during a seizure. Once it stopped, she and Steve laughed together about the humor they found in the situation. "They are one unit, in tune with each other, accepting, and laughing with each other," says Bellinda.

On a Friday afternoon, a mere six months into treatment, Dr. Morgan called Steve with some bad news about Becky's recent MRI. She was concerned, because it appeared that the cancer had returned. They couldn't be sure until Dr. Butowski had a chance to look at the MRI the following week, when he returned to the office.

Dr. Butowski reviewed the MRI and called Steve to let him know that Becky was still stable. What they had thought was a tumor was actually accumulated scar tissue. He gave Steve his personal phone number and permission to contact him at any time.

CHAPTER 13
A New Season of Caregiving

In the summer of 2007, Steve retired from his role as chief executive officer of the Midwest Banking Region for Regions Financial Corp., at the age of fifty-seven.

The story of his departure made local news. John Ketzenberger of the *Indianapolis Star* reported about Steve's banking career: "He proved his executive mettle when Indiana National Bank was on the verge of collapse in the mid-1970s. Schenck's tenure at six banks began when Indiana National was acquired by NBD in the early 1990s. He thrived through eight acquisitions, eventually managing banks with 2,200 employees and more than $10 billion in assets" (*Indianapolis Star*, March 18, 2007).

The *Indianapolis Star* also covered the story of Steve's retirement party, which was attended by 300 people. Reporter Susan Guyett wrote: "Family, friends, financial execs from competing businesses, community leaders, Democrats, Republicans and everyone in between showed up to give the CPA a pat on the back in anticipation of his June 30 departure. Sorely missed at the party was Schenck's wife, Becky, who wasn't up to attending the bash. She has been battling brain cancer since last summer but had hoped to be there. The couple worked together on many community projects over the years. Employees chipped in and collected $7,500 that will be given to Christamore House for the Becky Schenck Early Childhood Education Center" (*Indianapolis Star*, May 20, 2007).

Steve had enjoyed his thirty-seven-year career in the banking industry, but now he knew it was time for his life to change. Becky was, and had always been, his number one priority. By retiring, he could commit himself fully to caring for her.

Steve stepped into his new role as Becky's sole caregiver. His devotion to Becky was unwavering, and Becky's love for Steve grew deeper as he cared for her every need. "Steve is as optimistic as he can be. He has given his life to this whole cause," says Dr. Morgan. "I wish all patients had a Steve. He adapted his modus operandi to moving her through the process. Steve is gracious and genuinely appreciative of all, even when people are just gentle in taking Becky's vitals. He notices that and appreciates it."

Steve learned so much about GBM in the process of caring for Becky's medical needs that he could read and interpret the radiologists' reports before the doctor had even called with the results. The doctors joked that he practically could be a doctor himself.

"Steve has a high character. Not everyone would make that degree of sacrifice. You find out what you're made of when you face adversity, and I found out what he's made of," says Dr. Kelly. "He put everything on hold when it came to Becky. He made sure she had the best…He devoted everything to his wife."

Each morning, the former executive helped his bride to bathe and dress. Even in her illness, it was important to Becky that she hold onto her love for fashion and looking her best.

When her clothes began to hang too loosely on her increasingly slender body, Steve took her shopping at her favorite stores for fashionable replacements. He became adept at applying her makeup for her each day. He drove her to doctor's appointments, took her to the nail salon for weekly manicures, and to her hair stylist to care for her wigs.

> ## "I have learned to celebrate all of the moments with Becky, even when things are tough."
>
> Steve Schenck

Whether or not a patient's spouse is in a position to become a full-time caregiver like Steve was for Becky, the demands of the role are heavy. "Caregivers are often keeping up all of their prior roles and taking on some, if not all of those given up by the patient," explains Page. "Caregivers need to look and find good support, accept help, and make sure to take care of themselves, give themselves a break. They need to take care of their own health, find an outsider, professional if necessary, to process the ups and downs of the disease with, and cope with the serious nature of the illness."

"Steve was an amazing husband to Becky before she got sick, but through this whole experience, I've realized how much he loves her; how devoted he is; how many sacrifices he has made," says Mary Beth. "He's a wonderful husband."

Eating in restaurants had always been one of Steve and Becky's favorite things to do. Now that Steve was home with Becky, they decided together on a place to dine out several times during the week. When Becky had the energy, they frequented their favorite spots: Ruth's Chris Steakhouse, Daddy Jack's, Mitchell's Fish Market. The management and staff at Ruth's Chris grew to love the couple who visited their restaurant often, and greeted them with hugs and interest in how Becky was faring. The restaurant's piano player knew them by name. On days when neither of them felt like eating in a restaurant, they ordered at the drive-through at Steak-n-Shake, parked in the restaurant's parking lot, and shared burgers and fries. Other times, Steve tapped the skills he had learned growing up in his family's Evansville burger joint, Leo's Big Boy Restaurant, and grilled burgers for the two of them, at home.

"Steve is salt to the earth," reflects Dr. Kelly. "If every spouse conducted themselves like Steve, it would be something. He put his life on hold to provide Becky with the best possible care."

Looking from the outside in, some might have wondered if Steve was pouring too much into his caregiving role. Not a chance, says Steve. "There's an assumption that caring for Becky full-time is a burden," he explains. "It's not. It's a gift, not an obligation. I take care of myself by taking care of her. I have learned to celebrate all of the moments with Becky, even when things are tough. This experience has deepened our love. When I get challenged or am teetering on depression, I just think of what Becky's going through and tell myself, 'come on man.'" The real hero is Becky, he says. "She is the one who inspires me with her attitude."

CHAPTER 14
Home, Where the Heart is

The progression of Becky's disease had caused Steve and Becky to re-examine what was most important to them. "This whole experience has solidified our faith," Steve told *Indianapolis Woman*. In the 2007 interview, he shared, "Work just does not take the priority it once did...material things just don't seem to matter. In the hierarchy, faith is number one, then spending time with family."

The Schencks made the decision in 2011 to move out of their dream home, in an effort to simplify their lives. They worked closely with their builder to design and construct a downsized home that would incorporate the things they loved most about their previous house, but with practicality being a top priority for their now different lifestyle. They moved into the new house in 2013.

The vast majority of the living space occupied the first floor; perfect for their needs. A main floor deck overlooked the built-in swimming pool, making it easy to watch the grandchildren having fun. A home gym allowed Steve to continue his workouts without leaving Becky.

The feel and design of the home was important, too. It needed to be a place of comfort and refuge for the uncertain times ahead. The Schencks' designer of many years, Tom Myer, used soft, neutral colors to create a light, peaceful ambiance in the home where Steve and Becky would spend many hours together.

Everywhere you look, Becky's own flair for style and design is evident. The house is full of light and windows and countless pieces of artwork that add soft touches of color and personality. The original watercolor painting above the stone fireplace depicts a country scene that reminded Becky of her childhood home in Princeton, Indiana.

Steve's home office is equipped for professional work, but what you notice most in the room are the framed photo prints of

various sizes; some color, some black and white. All of them are images of family, and most of them are memories he cherishes from his life with Becky. It's a pictorial trove of remembrances. There's not a hint of wistfulness as Steve describes the candid shots of a healthy, gorgeous Becky in sequined evening gowns. Not a trace of melancholy for any days past. There is instead a unique and touching sense of complete adoration for this woman whom he cherishes every bit as much now, despite the difficult season of life.

The watercolor painting in the Schencks' home reminded Becky of her childhood home (Photo courtesy of *Indianapolis Woman* and PULSPhotography).

CHAPTER 15

Sharing the Journey

"I realize how good life is and how much we have to be thankful for, even in a time of challenge. My job is to see that we cherish each day."

Steve Schenck, in an interview with
Indianapolis Woman

At each step of the way, it was important to Steve and Becky to share their experience with others. They accepted an invitation to talk with journalist Anne Ryder, for the February 2007 issue of *Indianapolis Woman* magazine. Becky was featured on the publication's cover. The four-page spread inside included family photos and a picture of the blue cooler that friends used to deliver meals to the Schencks. In the article, Steve said, "I realize how good life is and how much we have to be thankful for, even in a time of challenge. My job is to see that we cherish each day."

There were many treasured moments and days. For the first several years following Becky's first surgery, Steve threw an annual Celebration of Life party for Becky, at their home on Geist Reservoir, to commemorate each year that she had beat her cancer. "Every day was a blessing," says Steve. "The time since the cancer are some of the best years that we have had." The parties were elegant and grand. "It was like a wedding reception," remembers Steve. Over one hundred guests filled the house and poured out into the backyard. Steve and Becky's friends, and even Becky's doctors, attended. From the catered food to the live band music, the events were natural gestures of gratitude and a heartfelt celebration of God's goodness to their family. "Everybody wanted to be part of those celebrations because Becky was such a special person," says her friend, Mary Beth.

Becky's "Dream Team" doctors became dear to her and to Steve, and the couple expressed their appreciation to them whenever and however they could. "Becky is so appreciative. They both are. They are very aware of how lucky she has been," says Dr. Morgan. Knowing that Dr. Berger was a huge football fan, Steve, one year, hosted Dr. Berger and his son for a trip to the Super Bowl.

CHAPTER 16
Family and Faith

A terminal illness like GBM affects more than just the patient. Everyone in a family is touched by the disease. "Patients (and families for that matter) need optimism balanced with reality, emotional support (counseling) around coping with a life-threatening illness and at times loss, loss of roles, of a 'life' or of a plan or expectation for what life was going to be like. This disease touches the whole family," says Page. So, it was natural that each of the Schencks' adult children processed Becky's advanced condition differently.

The Schencks' daughter, Julie (pictured right, with Becky), was living at home when Becky was diagnosed with GBM, in 2006.

At the time of Becky's diagnosis, their two oldest children, Jim and Scott, were married. Their daughter, Julie (Garvin), was only twenty-two and living at home. She described her relationship with her mom to *Indianapolis Woman*. "We have grown to be best friends," she said in 2007. "I never thought we'd be in a situation where she would be dependent on me. It's a big role. A very

Steve and Becky's daughter, Julie Garvin (pictured far right), is grateful for the time she had with her parents (photo courtesy *Indianapolis Woman* and PULSPhotography).

special role." In the same article, Julie shared that the whole experience had brought her closer to her dad, too.

"When we first found out [about the diagnosis], it was devastating, and I was so young. Someone says your mom has six months to live. You think of the worst case scenario. But this is a slow, painful process, as you see someone decrease over such a long period of time...You have to take each day as it is and have the expectation that it's not going to get any better, but that I still have her around."

Becky enjoyed spending time with her children. She's pictured here with her son, Andy Schenck.

Andy continued the close relationship that he had always shared with his mom, even when it became harder to communicate with her. He says he's grateful for the time that they've spent together.

Having gone through the cancer experience with his mom, Andy offers this advice to other patients diagnosed with brain cancer: "Fight. Don't give up...Yes, my mom has advantages and there are resources out there. She's beating it and anyone can do that. You just have to find the resources. Duke University Medical Center is doing something now in which they inject the tumor with the polio virus and it's been somewhat successful.[9] Doctors are practicing medicine. So each one has a different opinion."

Jim says, "We're all terminal. None of us knows how much time we have. My mother has been living her life to the fullest, and that's more than anyone can ask for."

Scott believes that Steve and Becky's relationship has been a vital part of Becky's battle with GBM. "Above all else, they are best friends, which is the foundation of every good relationship," he says. "My dad is good at problem solving on the fly, and he is able to know what my mom is trying to say. He's always there for her."

Becky's friends and family members were inspired by her unshakeable faith in God and His plan for her life. She freely and often shared her survival story and the source of her hope. "I have brain cancer," she'd tell the waitress or grocery store clerk, or anyone else. "I thank God every day for my life."

"She was really proud to be a cancer survivor," says Steve. Becky's friend, Mary Beth, reflects, "It's her attitude of faith, that she's going to overcome. Becky would say that the reason that she has been able to go on for ten years is because of God. She would also say that God is the only reason she has overcome any challenge in her life. She has a very steady faith, which is just remarkable. Her faith and hope drive her."

CHAPTER 17

Inspiring Others

Becky always looked for opportunities to use her experience to encourage others. Gretchen, one of the receptionists at IU Health, was one of those people. She quickly noticed Becky's fortitude and positive attitude. While Becky sat in the waiting room before her chemotherapy appointments, Gretchen watched her as she shared her story with other cancer patients and encouraged them to stay strong.

"Throughout all of this, she has never seen herself as a victim, even though this was described to her as terminal in the beginning."

Dr. Jennifer Morgan

Becky reached out to other glioblastoma patients and offered them hope for a fulfilling life. "Becky even met with some of my other GBM patients," explains Dr. Morgan. "One patient used to be a hard-working, strong man. He was now in a nursing home. Becky sat with him, held his hand, and knew exactly what he was going through. That made a world of difference. She connected with him. She did that for several of my patients. Throughout all of this, she has never seen herself as a victim, even though this was described to her as terminal in the beginning. Becky always had a wonderfully positive disposition."

"She's a warrior. She has a will that's amazing. She has an insatiable confidence to never give up."

Bryan Mills, CEO, Community Health Network

The staff members at Community North Hospital, where Becky was also receiving treatment, began to notice the amazing, positive attitude of the "resilient little lady who was defying the odds." In the face of a painful, debilitating disease, she exhibited kindness and patience. She never felt sorry for herself and always put others' needs before her own.

Stories about the impact Becky was making on those around her made their way to Bryan Mills, the chief executive officer of Community Health Network. He was looking for a motivating presenter for the Voice of Hope annual conference, featuring the organization's top 1,000 employees. He knew Steve from the business community and from his involvement with the United Way. Mills invited Becky to be the keynote speaker.

As she took the stage, the lively ballroom full of doctors, nurses, technicians, and support staff fell silent. Becky shared her story of hope in the face of a terrible prognosis. She shared her faith in God. She spoke of the exceptional medical care she had received. She let them know how much it meant to receive smiles and hugs, and to be treated not as another sick client, but as a whole person. Years after this speech, the staff at Community Health Network still refers to Becky's story. "She's a warrior," says Mills. "She has a will that's amazing. She has an insatiable confidence to never give up."

When Steve co-chaired the 2012 United Way of Central Indiana fundraising campaign, the leadership role became another platform to inspire others with the story of Becky's ongoing battle with the cancer that should have claimed her life years earlier. Steve shared some of the details of their story in a blog article on the organization's website:

"It was uncomfortable for me to have people dropping off food to the porch of our Geist home. I remember telling Becky, 'We don't need this. We can take care of this by ourselves.' Becky disagreed. She understood there are two sides to giving. We did need to know that Becky was surrounded by caring people who were contributing to her healing and to mine and not just with delicious, ready-to-eat meals. With faith, family, and friends, we are celebrating six years of survival this month. I picture that blue and white cooler whenever I am tempted to talk about United Way with people…What we do together to improve our community amounts to calling on our best and highest values. We help caring people see and understand the challenges in our community, and see their neighbors as people with needs that we can tackle together."[10]

In a fundraising video for the campaign, Steve and Becky expressed their gratitude to Lilly for their groundbreaking research and for the clinical trial that had such a big impact on Becky's prognosis. They used their story to encourage donations to United Way, an organization that shares their own commitment to giving and helping the community. The video ended with a spontaneous, poignant moment, as Becky turned to Steve and said, "I love you." He turned to her, grinned, and said, "I love you, too."[11]

CHAPTER 18
Defying the Odds

Between 2007 and early 2013, Becky's bimonthly MRIs showed no change and she continued to do well. She and Steve were grateful as, with each passing year, she far surpassed her prognosis. Dr. Berger and Dr. Butowski place Becky in an elite group of GBM patients who outlive the average prognosis; they estimate perhaps as small as five percent. Her great surgery, compliance with direction, experimental meds, and overall health enhanced her initial twelve- to fifteen-month prognosis.

At any opportunity, Becky and Steve were quick to express their gratitude to Lilly for the company's trial drug that had helped Becky survive. In 2009, *Indianapolis Business Journal* published Steve's letter in its Opinion section. In it, he wrote, "…you see, my wife, Becky, is alive today because of Lilly and its trial drug…a great surgeon, and a terrific team of local doctors" (*Indianapolis Business Journal*, March 30, 2009).

In 2010, Becky accepted an invitation to speak to the global research team at Lilly about her experience in the clinical trial. Physically, the speaking engagement was a push, as

Becky battled overwhelming fatigue, but she was determined to give back to the company whose research had helped to extend her life. She was very excited to have the opportunity.

Speaking from an auditorium at Lilly's Indianapolis corporate headquarters, she addressed an audience of more than a hundred researchers and employees. As she spoke, her remarks were broadcast live to Lilly researchers across the globe. She expressed her gratitude for the company's important research and for the opportunity to participate in the clinical trial. She shared the hope that a clinical trial offers someone like her, who is faced with terminal brain cancer.

The researchers wanted to know all about how she felt physically, taking the experimental drug. She gladly described not only her physical experience, but also her spiritual one. She openly shared her faith and the source of her hope, despite her terminal diagnosis. The audience was moved by her positive outlook and inspired by her story. During the question-and-answer session that followed her speech, the first question posed to Becky was about her faith and church affiliation. She left the event feeling physically exhausted, but exhilarated.

Her condition was stable during this period of time, but the seven years were by no means easy. There were the long flights to San Francisco, the many seizures, and the constant threat of the cancer returning. Becky could no longer drive a car, and the loss of her independence was extremely difficult. But she was fighting hard against her disease and defying the odds.

When they returned home, on the day of Becky's 2010 speaking engagement at Lilly, Steve received a call from Dr. Butowski. He instructed Steve to have Becky stop taking the chemotherapy drug. Although it had been successfully fighting the cancer for the past three-and-a-half years, Becky's lab results gave the doctor cause for concern. Her platelet and red and white blood cell counts were dangerously outside of a healthy range. He worried that if she continued taking the medication, it would destroy more than just her cancer; it would destroy the rest of her body, too. Dr. Butowski believed that stopping the chemo would not necessarily result in the cancer's return. "This was a big deal for us, because Becky was beating the odds," explains Steve. "We wanted this success to continue." It did, for a few precious more years.

CHAPTER 19

Continuing the Fight

On a July evening in 2013, Steve and Becky's worst fear came true. Becky was eating her meal at a local restaurant, when suddenly, her face went blank. Her eyelids fluttered, while her face became impassive. Steve knew. The cancer was back.

By the next morning, Steve had another MRI in his hands. The hazy, light-grey mass had returned. The tumor had grown anew.

The news was devastating, but Steve and Becky still refused to give up hope. "Becky is a remarkable human being," shares Mary Beth. "I've never known someone like that, who just never wants to give up; who's tough as nails, but at the same time, has the biggest heart of anyone you'd ever want to meet."

Later that week, Steve sat down at his computer and wrote to his family and friends:

Dear Friends,

It is hard to believe that it was seven years ago when Becky was diagnosed with stage four brain cancer

(GBM)...She was given a year to fifteen months. This week, it was determined that her brain cancer has returned. Becky is clearly a miracle, and our family has been so blessed to be able to share this amazing journey. The good news is that we have engaged our same team of doctors to help us make our next journey. It will begin on Wednesday, when we go to San Francisco for her surgery, which will be on Thursday, at the University of California, San Francisco. Dr. Mitch Berger, Chairman of the Department of Neurological Surgery, will perform the surgery. He is amazing and the best surgeon in this regard. Dr. Nicholas Butowski, also at UCSF, will be Becky's Neuro-Oncologist. He managed the trial drug from Lilly, following her last surgery. Our local team continues with Dr. Jennifer Morgan, IU Health Cancer Center, and Dr. Tim Kelly, Community Health Network.

Our family is well aware of the challenging times in front of us...but we have managed before, with our focus on faith, family, and friends...we will continue to stay the course. Your prayers are welcome!!

Positive regards,

Steve

Friends and family poured out their support. Letters and flowers arrived at the house almost daily. Within a few days, Becky was back in San Francisco for surgery. The operation went well and again, Becky recovered quickly. Her family noticed that her speech and memory were affected more by this second surgery than the first. She had more difficulty carrying on a conversation, and she struggled even more with short-term memory loss.

By January of 2015, Becky's cancer returned yet again. She had a third surgery and was able to do a second round of radiation, as well. She went back on chemotherapy, this time taking two different types of drugs. A mere three months later, her doctors determined that she needed to stop the chemotherapy, as her blood work had returned to alarming levels.

The two additional surgeries and second round of radiation greatly reduced Becky's ability to process speech. Becky's core personality remained the same, but she struggled with balance issues, memory loss, and very limited speech. She found activities that she enjoyed doing around the house, and spent long hours gardening and tending to the flowers. She struggled to string together short sentences.

This latter development was hard for Becky's family and friends. She was still Becky, but she could barely communicate. It was difficult for her, too. There were so many things she wanted to say to those around her, but the words became increasingly difficult. But Steve was there, at her side. He patiently listened to her, looked into her big brown eyes, tried to figure out what she was trying to say, and verbalized it for her, with an amazing degree of accuracy.

"They truly have made the best of this situation."

Jennifer Morgan, M.D., IU Health

Steve and Becky remained upbeat and maintained their sense of humor, even when it came to difficulties like memory loss. One afternoon, Steve took Becky to the shopping mall. His mobile phone rang, and he knew that he needed to answer an important call. Out of the corner of his eye, he saw Becky walk over to a makeup counter. By the time he finished the call, she was holding a small makeup bag. Steve asked her what she had bought. "I have no idea," Becky said. Steve laughed, "Well I hope you bought the right colors." He loved seeing her happy.

"They are able to see the humor in situations," says Dr. Morgan. "He's painting her eyeliner and she's telling him he's doing it crooked, then they're laughing. They giggle together after all they've gone through. They truly have made the best of this situation."

"It's a remarkable love story to me. It's a love story about two people who are completely committed and devoted to one another," says their friend, Mary Beth.

CHAPTER 20
Preparing for the End

The most difficult news yet about Becky's deteriorating condition descended on a frosty evening in February of 2016. Becky had suffered an accidental fall and her doctor prescribed an MRI. Test results showed that the tumor had grown exponentially in the six short weeks since the last image had been taken. A phone call with Dr. Butowski confirmed that neither surgery nor radiation were options, given Becky's frail physical condition. There was nothing more that could be done for the patient whom he had cared for over the past nine years of treating her disease. It was time to explore options for hospice care.

The news fell hard on both Steve and Becky, and on their family. They were about to enter the final stages of Becky's journey. They had known that this day would come, but it was nonetheless difficult to process.

Once again, the team at UCSF became a welcome resource. Page, who had been Becky's nurse during the clinical trial, had since assumed her role as nurse coordinator for UCSF's Neuro-Oncology Gordon Murray Caregiver Program.

The program was designed to support families and caregivers by providing them with education, information, access to disease and caregiver resources, as well as information and referral to peer and professional counseling and support groups. Page sent Steve a digital copy of UCSF's *Transitions in Care for Patients with Brain Tumors: Palliative and Hospice Care,* that includes valuable information

UCSF Caregiver Resources

Steve and Becky received tremendous support from the neuro-oncology team at UCSF. The medical organization has created a valuable collection of resources for brain cancer patients and their families. To explore these helpful tools, visit http://www.ucsfhealth.org.

on everything from specific brain tumor symptoms to advance care planning to grief and bereavement. It's one of many practical, helpful resources available to the public on the UCSF website (http://www.ucsfhealth.org).

Just as they had done at every other juncture, Steve and Becky began to plan for what lay ahead of them. They made a list of things they wanted to attend in the coming weeks; grandchildren's sports events, dinners at their favorite spots, time with their kids. While she was able, Becky wanted to be an active participant in the life she loved.

With Steve at her side, Becky made it to the grandkids' gymnastics meets and basketball games. On Easter Sunday, she and Steve hosted an egg hunt for all eight of the grandchildren at their home.

On the days when Becky felt up to it, she and Steve continued their dinner dates at nice restaurants around Indianapolis. Each time, Steve asked the servers to capture a photo of them on his iPhone.

On most days, Steve asked Becky the question that had become a welcome, daily ritual. "Where should we have lunch today, Red?" Her eyes searched his face for the answer she struggled to convey with words. Without hesitation, Steve always offered up two or three alternatives, then suggested one of them. On the occasions when Becky was tired and she and Steve didn't want to mess with applying her makeup, he'd volunteer a fast-food option. "How about if we try Steak-n-Shake today?" he asked on a sunny spring morning. Becky's eyes lit up. "Steak-n-Shake! Great!" she said with enthusiasm.

Steve tilted his fist up in the air with a playful gesture of affection. Becky lifted her fist to meet his own, for a gentle "fist bump" that sealed their agreement. Their lunch date would be burgers and fries, enjoyed in the privacy of their car. "What's significant is that we love every minute of it," Steve says.

As Becky's health declined, she and Steve still ate dinner at their favorite Indianapolis restaurants whenever possible.

Steve began to research options for Becky's home hospice care. He wanted the very best. He interviewed and hired a caring hospice provider from St. Vincent Hospital. She visited twice each week, administering Becky's pain medications and tending to her physical and emotional needs. Another caregiver spent a few hours each week with Becky, too. Her short visits allowed Steve to begin working on other details for the remaining weeks he and Becky anticipated sharing together, and the difficult ones that would follow her passing.

According to Page, hospice is a vital part of the brain cancer journey. "Hospice is critical, because it is a specialized type of care that is provided by a team of professionals who are skilled at caring for someone, and their family, in their last months of life," she says. "The focus changes from treatment to comfort and maximizing quality of life. Managing symptoms so a patient does not suffer is of primary importance, as is providing information about what lies ahead for the patient and family and helping patients and families deal with the spiritual aspects of life and death. Hospice providers have chosen this as their specialty and are often passionate about making this part of the illness as good as it can be."

Steve embarked on the painful work of planning for the end of Becky's journey. At each step of the way, he and Becky had always looked for ways to use their experience to touch, encourage, and inspire others. This stage would be no different.

He immediately envisioned a large event that would follow Becky's passing. It would be a celebration of her life that would bring together many of the people whose lives she had touched during her hard-fought battle with glioblastoma. It would be held close to home, at their neighborhood's clubhouse. Steve and the kids agreed that it should include Becky's favorite things: family, good food, good music, and good friends. At the piano would be the musician from Ruth's Chris Steakhouse, who had so often played Becky's special requests. There would be sunflowers, of course. It would be beautiful, elegant, and joyful, just like the woman that the occasion would honor.

On the day that would follow, Becky would be laid to rest in a spot Steve had chosen for the love of his life. A small, private funeral would give the family precious time to grieve their loss together.

CHAPTER 21

Beyond Words

An unusually warm spring enabled the Schencks to open their underground swimming pool by mid-April of 2016. Steve worked hard to make it happen, envisioning how much Becky would enjoy watching the grandchildren swimming in their backyard.

A cloudless, blue sky and temperatures near eighty degrees made for a perfect Saturday afternoon. All four of the Schencks' children and eight grandchildren gathered for a mid-afternoon swim. Steve manned the grill and Becky sat in the shade of the patio umbrella, as the kids splashed in the pool. As best she could, she managed to eat a ketchup-smothered hot dog.

It had been a scene similar to this one, ten years ago, when their lives had changed so drastically. On that day in 2006, the Schencks never could have imagined that Becky would commence her hard-fought battle for life. For a decade, she had beaten the odds and far outlived her initial prognosis. On this spring day in 2016, her health was failing and the words she could utter were few. She was nearing the end.

Yet, in Becky's characteristic fashion, she pushed herself to participate in this poolside gathering with her family. She had not given up.

In the days that followed this sunny scene, her health continued to fail, as the end drew nearer. Walking became difficult. Eating lost its pleasure.

Even so, moments of life and light offset the growing shadows of the cancer's progression.

The staff at the Christamore House worked to keep the memory of Becky's contributions alive and well, within the organization and with the children at the Early Childhood Center. As an expression of their gratitude, the kids hand-painted a portrait of a sunny nature scene for Becky. A three-dimensional paper monarch attached to the painting created the impression that the Monarch was ready to soar beyond the confines of its canvas habitat. The staff sent the artwork, along with a framed photo of the children, to the Schencks' home. It was a welcome delivery that brought tears to Becky's eyes.

A couple of months later, with Becky's health declining rapidly, the Christamore House reached out to the Schencks again. This time, in the form of an invitation to attend the organization's annual awards luncheon. They had named Becky the recipient of the 2016 Martha Stewart Carey Award, in recognition of her exemplary contributions to Christamore House and her commitment and dedication to furthering its mission. The gesture encouraged and touched Becky and Steve. Making it to the event would be impossible, so the Schencks' son, Andy, attended the luncheon and accepted the award in his mom's honor.

Steve commissioned a writer to craft an obituary for the inevitable day to come.

Becky received the gift of a painting from the children at the Christamore House Early Education Center in spring 2016.

The day would come, when Becky's journey would be complete. But for now, there was yet another day of life to be lived. There was joy to be found. There was time yet to be together. And for that gift, Becky and Steve felt gratitude beyond words.

Notes

1. "Steve and Becky Schenck: Lilly United Way e-card," YouTube video, 3:34, October 8, 2012, posted by United Way of Central Indiana, https://www.youtube.com/watch?v=4QdC3orlfZM.

2. American Brain Tumor Association, "Brain Tumor Statistics," (accessed March 30, 2016) http://www.abta.org/about-us/news/brain-tumor-statistics/.

3. National Center for Biotechnology Information, "Beyond the World Health Organization grading of infiltrating Gliomas: Advances in the Molecular Genetics of Glioma Classification," Krishanthan Vigneswaran, Stewart Neill, and Costas G. Hadjipanayis, (accessed March 30, 2016) http://www.NCBI.nlm.nih.gov/pmc/articles/PMC4430738/.

4. American Association of Neurological Surgeons, "Glioblastoma Multiforme," (accessed March 30, 2016) http://www.aans.org/patient%20information/conditions%20and%20treatments/glioblastoma%20multiforme.aspx/.

5. University of California San Francisco Medical Center, "Brain Mapping," (accessed March 31, 2016) https://www.ucsfhealth.org/treatments/brain_mapping/.

6. Becky Schenck, interview by Anne Marie Tiernon, November 28, 2014, WTHR, Indianapolis,Indiana.

7. Julie Schenck Garvin (daughter of Steve and Becky Schenck), interview by Anne Ryder, *Indianapolis Woman*, February 2007, Indianapolis, Indiana.

8. GiveForward Inc., "Financial Assistance for Cancer Patients," (accessed March 31, 2016), http://www.giveforward.com/p/financial-assistance-for-cancer-patients.

9. Duke University Medical Center, "Targeting Cancer with Genetically Engineered Poliovirus (PVS-RIPO)," Matthias Grimier, M.D. and Gordon Vlahovic, M.D., M.H.S., (accessed April 4, 2016), http://www.cancer.duke.edu/btc/modules/Research3/index.php?id=41.

10. Steve Schenck, "Live United: The Difference Between a Good Return and an Abundant One," July 13, 2012, http://www.uwci.org/news/live-united-the-difference-between-a-good-return-and-an-abundant-one/.

11. "Steve and Becky Schenck: Lilly United Way e-card," YouTube video, 3:34, October 8, 2012, posted by United Way of Central Indiana, https://www.youtube.com/watch?v=4QdC3orlfZM.

Resources

Glioblastoma Multiforme (GBM) at a Glance   18

Brain Mapping   23

Caregiving Following a Diagnosis   24

Financial Assistance Resources   28

UCSF Caregiver Resources   64